Rational Emotive
Behavior Therapy

Shame

Revised

Tim Sheehan, Ph.D.

HAZELDEN

The following titles compose the complete REBT learning program. Each is available in booklet, workbook, audio, and video format:

Understanding • *Anger* • *Perfectionism*
Anxiety and Worry • *Depression* • *Shame*
Grief • *Guilt* • *Self-Esteem*

Hazelden
Center City, Minnesota 55012-0176

Second edition 2002
Printed in the United States of America

ISBN: 1-56838-952-3

The stories in this workbook are composites of many individuals. Any similarity to any one person is purely coincidental.

About the workbook
In trying to understand our feelings in recovery, we often discover that we carry a great deal of shame. Whether our shame is rooted in our childhood or is a direct result of our addiction, we can learn to work through our shame and have a healthier, happier life. This workbook provides an effective guide for doing so, by using Rational Emotive Behavior Therapy (REBT).

Dr. Albert Ellis, who first articulated Rational-Emotive Therapy (RET) in the 1950s, changed the name in the 1990s to Rational Emotive Behavior Therapy (REBT) to more accurately reflect the role behavior plays in gauging changes in thinking. While the therapeutic approach remains the same, the pamphlets, workbooks, audios, and videos in this series have been changed to reflect the updated name.

About the author
Timothy J. Sheehan, Ph.D., is Vice President, Academic Affairs, for the Hazelden Foundation's Education Division.

Dr. Sheehan holds a Doctorate Degree in Clinical Psychology and has held numerous positions over the past twenty years at Hazelden, including leadership roles in clinical psychology and health care services, as well as administrative roles in adult, youth, and transitional care. He is the author of a sequence of pamphlets and workbooks addressing the application of Rational Emotive Behavior Therapy for depression and shame as well as *Facing an Eating Disorder in Recovery* and *Freedom from Compulsion: An Eating Disorder Workbook*. He is also the author of "The Disease Model" in McCrady and Epstein's *Addictions: A Comprehensive Guidebook*. He is a professor in Hazelden's Graduate School in Addiction Studies and an adjunct associate professor in the graduate school of psychology at St. Mary's University of Minnesota.

Introduction

Those of us recovering from emotional problems and addictions sometimes feel empty or long to be fulfilled. Although we have given up on addictive behaviors as the solution to our problems in living, something may seem to be missing. Understanding our feelings is often a confusing task, since many of us have taken care to keep ourselves numb—that is, with no feelings—rather than feeling distressed. How do we sidestep our feelings of shame?

- Some of us have avoided looking *too* closely at ourselves for fear of what we might find.
- Others of us have almost unknowingly refused to accept ourselves and instead often negate our self-worth through endlessly comparing ourselves with friends, acquaintances, and family members.
- Still others of us have attempted to rebuild these feelings of shame through rigid perfectionism.

The origin of our shame

Feelings of shame stem from negative self-evaluations that undermine our self-confidence. Often these negative self-evaluations are rooted in childhood experiences in which we were not nurtured as a valuable person, and thus we falsely concluded that we were worthless. Some of us have also learned negative self-evaluation in responses to the painful effects of addiction. The more we tried to quit using chemicals, and the more our efforts failed, the more we devalued our self-worth. Some of us speak of shame as if we were born predisposed to think negatively of ourselves and our abilities. Although we may achieve a number of important goals, we never seem quite good enough to ourselves.

Taking charge

While shame may stem from different causes or sources, we can help ourselves to feel better, accept our worth, and enhance our self-confidence by taking charge of our thoughts, feelings, and behavior. That is what this workbook is all about. In the pages ahead we will examine some of our negative self-evaluations and explore ways to change our thoughts and behaviors.

Learning about our feelings and behavior

Since our shame often leaves us feeling numb or fearful of our emotions, let's begin by increasing our self-awareness. Feelings are sensations resulting from our mind-body connection. Feelings can

The *ABC* process described in this workbook is based on the work of Dr. Albert Ellis and his Rational Emotive Behavior Therapy.

best be described in a short phrase—often, one word is all you need to label your emotions. Four words cover the range of feelings—*sad*, *mad*, *glad*, and *scared*—but many of us use different words such as *pissed off* or *numbed out* to describe our feelings.

Filling in the blank, describe how you are feeling now.

Right now I feel____.

Next, think about the times that you have been aware of your feelings of shame. Some of us describe those feelings in terms of feeling empty, sad, numb, or unable to feel. The following exercise will help you get started:

- For me, shame feels like______________________________.

- I first became aware of my feeling of shame when__________

  ____.

- The last time I felt a surge of shame was________________

  ____.

- Now, I feel shameful when______________________________

  ____.

Feelings of shame are unpleasant in and of themselves. In addition, shame can keep us stuck and block us from making changes needed to live healthier, happier lives. When we feel shame intensively or over a long period of time, an urge often accompanies the discomfort: "I felt so ashamed that I just wanted to hide."

Feelings create urges ⟶ Urges motivate behavior

Our shame may make us feel an urgency to reduce our pain, but often in self-destructive ways. Sabotaging a relationship, isolating ourselves, hurting ourselves, compulsive drinking or eating, or having sex to avoid or forget feelings of shame are all examples of behaviors that dull the pain but fuel a continued sense of shame.

Take a few moments and list under the headings "Helpful" and "Harmful" some of the things you've done to stop your feelings of shame. Reflect on some of the things that have been helpful as well as those actions that were eventually harmful.

Helpful	*Harmful*
______________________________	______________________________
______________________________	______________________________
______________________________	______________________________
______________________________	______________________________
______________________________	______________________________

Learning to change our thinking

Let's continue by taking a closer look at some of the beliefs we hold about ourselves. When we put ourselves down, we are usually evaluating ourselves negatively. These self-evaluations are made up of our own thoughts and beliefs about ourselves. Thoughts are how we communicate with ourselves. Our feelings are largely based on our thoughts. It is our self-talk that triggers and reinforces our feelings of shame. When we put ourselves down through our negative self-evaluations, we are actually telling ourselves that there is something basically wrong with us. It isn't that we have made mistakes or that bad things have happened to us, it's that *we* tell ourselves we are the mistake, *we* are bad.

Here are some examples of negative self-evaluation, sometimes called *shame-based logic.*

- "My mother always told me I wouldn't make it, and she was right. What a loser I am."
- "I'll never measure up. The more I try, the more inadequate I am. Everyone must know by now how utterly worthless I am."
- "This lasagna is disgusting. I'm a lousy cook."

Think for a moment. Now write in the spaces at least two of your own examples of shame-based logic.

1. ____

____

2. ____

____

Our put-downs, our shame-based logic, our negative self-evaluations are all distortions of reality. They are myths—myths about ourselves. We can begin to empower ourselves and reduce our feelings of shame by disputing our myths, challenging our shame-based logic, changing our negative self-evaluations, and ending our self-imposed put-downs.

We dispute our logic by actively questioning our beliefs about ourselves. We attack our shame-based thinking by demanding proof or evidence to substantiate our beliefs. We question our negative self-evaluations and scrutinize our expectancies. We stop rating ourselves and our worth. Instead, we accept our value as a worthwhile, fallible person who deserves to be treated with dignity and respect.

Shame-based logic	*Questioning our beliefs*
My mother always told me I wouldn't make it, and she was right. What a loser I am.	Since when was my mother always right? Whose expectation is this anyway—mine? Where is the evidence that I am a loser? Lots of people, including me, have dealt with emotional problems and addiction—coping with these problems helps me to win rather than lose.
This lasagna is disgusting. I'm a lousy cook.	Why do I think I can't cook? The lasagna was disgusting because my oven doesn't work, not because I always fail at cooking. Lots of people who are good cooks have occasional failures, or they wouldn't know what to do to improve!

Give it a try. Question your shame-based logic in the following spaces.

Shame-based logic	*Questioning our beliefs*
______________________	______________________
______________________	______________________
______________________	______________________
______________________	______________________
______________________	______________________

Putting it all together

Now that we have a good start, let's put into action some of the principles we are learning. We will use a simple format to help us identify and change our thoughts, feelings, and behavior. *A* will stand for the event or situation associated with feelings of shame. *B* will represent our shame-based logic, those negative self-evaluations that trigger and reinforce our feelings.

Think of a recent event that you associate with feelings of shame. Write in the blank space following the example in section *A*, describing your own event. Take care to describe just the facts. Think of it as though you were taking a picture or making an audiotape. Avoid assumptions or impressions.

Example:

- I spoke with my mother on the phone yesterday—we agreed to have lunch, and she is now forty-five minutes late.

Your example:

A: *The event*

____

____

____

____

Now write an inventory of the thoughts that triggered your feelings, the negative self-evaluations and shame-based logic that fuel your feelings of shame. These myths distort reality and are often based on unrealistic demands, negative exaggerations, and excuses.

Examples:

- She should have been on time; she's being deliberately rude by being so late.
- She wouldn't be so late if I was important to her; she's probably busy doing something more important like ironing.
- Not even my mother cares about me. What is it about me that's so flawed?

Your example:

B: *Inventory*

____

____

____

Next, describe your feelings and urges in section *C*. Remember, feelings are mind-body sensations. They are different from thoughts. Feelings such as shame also entail an urge as well. These urges motivate our behavior. Identify your *feelings* at *C* as well as the *urge* or *behavior* that goes with them.

Example:

- Depressed, blue, shameful

Your example:

C: *Feelings*

____

____

____

Example:

- Order a bottle of wine and start drinking it immediately to take the edge off my shame.

Your example:

Urges

____

____

Take a good look at the shame-based logic you described in section *B*. Writing in the blank space after section *D*, dispute one by one each statement that was listed in *B*. Question the unrealistic demands, negative exaggerations, and excuses. Don't hesitate to talk back to yourself. You want to eventually change your negative self-evaluations to a more neutral or objective viewpoint.

Examples:

- My mother could be late for many reasons, perhaps none of which have anything to do with me.
- Even if my mother is late, perhaps is often late, how does that prove that *I'm* flawed?

Your example:

D: *Dispute your logic*

____

____

____

By debunking our negative self-evaluations, we *empower* ourselves to develop goals that can help us lead more productive, happy lives. In section *E* write out what you would like to have happen. For instance, a goal might read something like this: "To become more assertive with family members while experiencing as little shame as possible."

Examples:

- To reduce my shame by reclaiming my personal power and worth.
- To put the situation I face into proper perspective, not allowing it to ruin my day or preoccupy my thoughts and feelings for a week or even a day.

Your example:

E: *Goals*

____

____

____

In section *F*, we will list the actions we can take in order to reach our goal. We are no longer talking about thoughts or feelings, but behaviors. We can take constructive action instead of falling into self-defeating patterns from the past.

For example, if our goal is "to become more assertive with family members while experiencing as little shame as possible," the actions we can take to reach our goal might be to

- participate in an assertiveness training group at a community school
- practice asserting my opinion with family members at least once each day
- apply REBT principles by completing the self-help worksheet (see pages 9–10) to attack shame-based logic
- evaluate my progress with the help of my therapist at the end of the week

Now it is your turn. After reading the examples, list all the actions (*F*) you could take to reach your goals. Go ahead, be creative!

Examples:

- I can call to see if my mother is still at home. If I can't reach her, I can wait another fifteen minutes and then leave.
- I can sit back, relax, and read while I wait.
- If she is chronically late, and I haven't yet told her that I think it is disrespectful, I can do that in the future.

Your example:

F: *Actions*

____

____

____

____

Moving right along

You did it! You've worked through an REBT example. Now you are ready to progress in eliminating your shame-based logic by using the worksheet that follows. Remember, you will need to practice REBT principles before they help ease your discomfort and provide you with alternatives to old patterns of self-defeating behavior. Expect to feel a bit awkward when you begin to apply these self-help methods. Change, even when it's positive, can feel foreign to us. This awkward feeling is simply a sign that you are making progress.

REBT worksheet

A: *The event*

Think of a recent event that you associate with feelings of shame and write about it in the following space. Describe just the facts. Avoid assumptions or impressions.

____

____

____

____

B: *Inventory*

Write an inventory of the thoughts that triggered your feelings, such as negative self-evaluations, shame-based logic, unrealistic demands, negative exaggeration, and excuses.

____

____

____

____

C: *Feelings*

Now list the feelings that your thoughts (identified in *B*) triggered. Remember, feelings are mind-body sensations—they're different from thoughts.

____

____

____

____

Urges
List the urge or behavior that goes along with the feelings you described.

____

____

____

D: *Dispute your logic*
Question the unrealistic demands, negative exaggerations, and excuses stated in *B*. As you identify them, write them down. "Talk back" to yourself; change your negative self-evaluations to a more neutral objective viewpoint.

____

____

____

E: *Preferences or goals*
What are your personal preferences for the situation—that is, what would you like to have happen? Develop goals that allow you to lead a more productive, happy life.

____

____

____

F: *Actions I could take*
List all the actions you can take in order to reach your goal. Write out constructive actions—positive behavior—you can take instead of the self-defeating patterns from the past.

____

____

____